JOHANN SEBASTIAN BACH
arranged for piano, four-hands by GREG ANDERSON

Brandenburg Concerto No. 3 in G major
(BWV 1048)

AWKWARD FERMATA PRESS

Note to performers:

In contrast to Max Reger's four-hand arrangement of Bach's third Brandenburg concerto, this arrangement features a labyrinth of choreographed hand crossings designed to serve two purposes:

— to bring to life the conversational, jocular, and highly antiphonal spirit of the nine-voiced original.
— to more equitably distribute the thorny, virtuosic passagework between the performers.

While some of the fingerings may seem odd, they are often offered as guidance to prevent collisions between the pianists' hands. Similarly, choreographic cues are listed throughout the score, though some pianists may find different positions better suited to their bodies. Dynamics are merely suggestions.

- G.A.

© 2019 AWKWARD FERMATA PRESS.
All Rights Reserved.

Published by Awkward Fermata Press.
www.gregandersonpiano.com

Public performance licensed by ASCAP.

ISBN-13: 978-0-9830625-3-0

Brandenburg Concerto No. 3 in G major, BWV 1048

Arranged for piano, four-hands by
Greg ANDERSON

Johann Sebastian BACH

under

over

poco a poco cresc.

poco a poco cresc.

16

Adagio

(Either pianist may play the solo.)

improvisatory

poco a poco cresc. e accel.

broaden

If the secondo pianist performs
the solo, the primo pianist
should take over here.

molto rit.

molto rit.

20

CPSIA information can be obtained
at www.ICGtesting.com
Printed in the USA
BVHW010530070321
601463BV00003B/12